MARTHA SPEAKS
CONTENTS

Endless Expressions

Expressions are phrases that mean something besides the literal meaning of the words (Martha gets them confused sometimes). For example, when you *pull someone's leg,* you don't actually pull on his leg. It means you tease him. Once you know what they mean, expressions can add a little fun and interest to speaking and writing. Instead of just saying you are feeling well, you could say you are *fit as a fiddle.* Match the expressions below with their meanings and then see if you can use them in the sentences on the following page.

1.   Bite off more than you can chew   _____
2.   Fly off the handle   _____
3.   Dog-eared   _____
4.   Go back to the drawing board   _____
5.   In a pickle   _____
6.   In the doghouse   _____
7.   By the seat of your pants   _____
8.   Smell a rat   _____
9.   Let sleeping dogs lie   _____
10. Snug as a bug in a rug   _____
11. Throw in the towel   _____
12. Full of beans   _____

A.   Lose your temper
B.   In a lot of trouble
C.   To do something without planning
D.   To give up
E.   Try to do more than you are able to
F.   Lots of energy
G.   Well-used; for a book or magazine, with many pages bent or turned down
H.   Comfortable and warm
I.   To be suspicious
J.   In a mess; in a difficult situation
K.   Start again
L.   Don't bring something up if it's going to cause trouble

For answers, see page 32.

1. Even though Helen had lots of homework, she wanted to be part of the school play. "Don't _____, Helen," warned Mom.

2. Martha ran around in circles. "Come on, Helen. Hurry!" she said. "The free burger samples will be gone before we get there!" Helen shook her head. "Boy, Martha, you sure are _____ today!"

3. "But it was such a good idea," Alice said. "I was sure it would work. I guess we should just _____."
 "No," Helen replied, "I still want to do it. But I guess we have to _____ _____."

4. Martha and Helen were soaking wet, waiting under a tree at the playground. "There I was warm and dry at home," Martha said, "_____ _____, but you thought we should go for a walk!"
"I'm sorry, Martha," Helen said. "I didn't know it was supposed to rain." Just then they heard a rumble of thunder in the distance. "Oh no, now we're really_____!"

For answers, see page 32.

Playful Poems

A **poem** is a special kind of writing. The writer or poet chooses words for their sound and beauty, as well as for their meaning. Often the last words in a sentence rhyme, but not always. And sometimes when you say a poem out loud, the lines have a rhythm, like in a song. Poems are a fun way to play with words, sounds, ideas, and feelings.

Firedog Freddie was Helen's favorite book when she was little. It is a poem that tells the story of a firehouse dog. Can you finish the poem by adding the rhyming words from the word bank at the top of this page?

Firedog Freddie

Was an adventurous fellow.

He wore a hat that was red

And a coat that was _____.

When the fire bell rang,

He jumped to his feet.

He slid down the pole

And roared down the _____.

He climbed up the ladder

With a hose in his mitt

And put out each fire

Lickety _____.

Fill in the speech and thought bubbles to
tell a story, or compose a short poem.

Firedog Martha

Martha fell asleep listening to Helen read *Firedog Freddie* and dreamed a new version starring Martha. Finish Martha's poem using the word bank above and draw a picture of her fantasy on the next page.

Firedog Martha

Was the bravest dog around.

If a fire was burning,

That's where Martha could be _____.

Some firemen climb up ladders,

Some firemen use a hose,

But no one but our Martha

Fights fires with her _____.

She helped to put the fire out.

She buried burning embers.

Her dogged heroism

The town still _____.

The firemen were grateful.

They all shook Martha's paw.

"That nose is tops!" exclaimed the Chief.

"It fills me up with _____."

Blue Mangoes

Helen loves this silly poem. It is a good example of a poem that rhymes and has a strong rhythm. Unlike in a story, the sound of the words in a poem is just as important as what they mean. Can you add the rhyming words from the word bank to finish the poem?

Nicholas Mellow

Had just stepped outside

When a strange little fellow

Appeared by his _____.

"Blue mangoes! Blue mangoes!"

Urged Genghis McGee.

"Won't you please try one?

They're fresh and they're _____!"

Nick picked up a mango.

He gave it a poke.

"But mangoes aren't blue," he cried.

"Is this a _____?"

"These mangoes are special.

They come from the moon!

Here, have a bite.

I'll lend you my _____."

"Thanks, but no thanks.

These mangoes are funny.

The outside is wrinkly.

The inside is _____.

"They smell like a squid

Wrapped up in old socks.

Me, I'd prefer

A big bag of _____."

"If you don't try some,

I promise, I'll pout.

I'll hold in my breath

And I won't let it _____.

"I'll stamp around

And throw a big fit

If you don't try

Just one little_____."

"Okay, okay,

I'm a reasonable fellow.

I'll try them, I will,"

Sighed Nicholas _____.

And so poor Nick,

With a look of pure dread,

Took one tiny scoop,

Then suddenly _____:

"I'm sorry, dear Genghis,

I can't eat your mangoes blue.

For though you are my friend,

To myself I must be _____."

The Story of You

An **autobiography** is a unique story. It is the true story of your life (so far), written by you! Start writing on a separate sheet of paper for more room. Here are a few sentences to help you get started.

_____'S ASTONISHING AUTOBIOGRAPHY
[your name]

My life story is doggone unique! My name is _____. **I was**
[fill in your name here]

born on _____, **in** _____.
[birthday]   [city, state]

_____ .
[Tell funny or interesting story about you as a baby here.]

_____ .

I have _____ **people in my family. They are** _____
[number]

_____
[names of people]

_____ .

I also have _____ **pets in my family. They include** _____
[number]

_____ .
[names and type of pets]

I am in the _____ **grade at** _____ . **I live in** _____.
[grade]   [school]   [city, state]

My friends are _____ .
[names of friends]

When we're together, we like to _____
[list activities]

_____ .

An amazing thing that happened to me was _____

_____ .

My future is full of promising possibilities. The rest of my life story should be doggone amazing, too!

Alphabet Code

A *code* is a secret language that you make up by using signs or numbers in place of letters, or by switching the letters around. Not only are they fun to create, but using secret codes also helps you learn spelling, practice reading skills, and use logic and reasoning. Use the key below to decipher Martha's secret.

SECRET CODE

Use the key to decipher Martha's secret.

I A T E H E L E N ' S   S O C K .
9 1 20 5 8 5 12 5 14 19   19 15 3 11

P L E A S E   D O N ' T   T E L L !
16 12 5 1 19 5   4 15 14 20   20 5 12 12

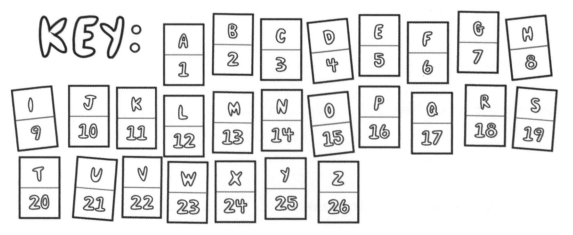

KEY:

A	B	C	D	E	F	G	H
1	2	3	4	5	6	7	8

I	J	K	L	M	N	O	P	Q	R	S
9	10	11	12	13	14	15	16	17	18	19

T	U	V	W	X	Y	Z
20	21	22	23	24	25	26

For answers, see page 32.

A Message to Martha

Now write your own message back to Martha using her secret code. Or create your own and write secret messages to your friends! You can fill in the key below with Martha's code or one of your own.

_____

_____

_____

_____

_____

_____

_____

KEY:

What's That Smell?

Martha loves to explore the world with her nose. It is full of so many delicious smells. Can you figure out all the words that have to do with smells and smelling?

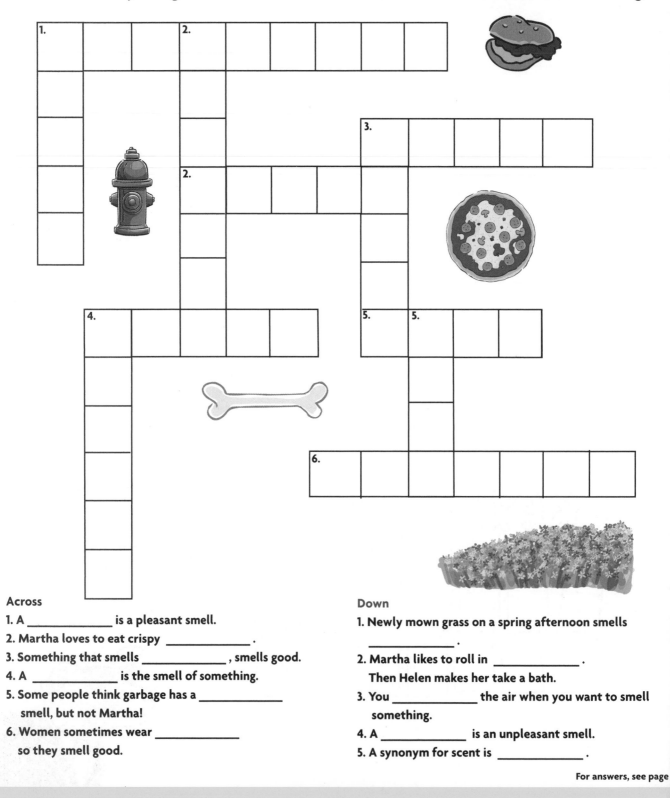

Across

1. A _____ is a pleasant smell.
2. Martha loves to eat crispy _____ .
3. Something that smells _____ , smells good.
4. A _____ is the smell of something.
5. Some people think garbage has a _____ smell, but not Martha!
6. Women sometimes wear _____ so they smell good.

Down

1. Newly mown grass on a spring afternoon smells _____ .
2. Martha likes to roll in _____ . Then Helen makes her take a bath.
3. You _____ the air when you want to smell something.
4. A _____ is an unpleasant smell.
5. A synonym for scent is _____ .

For answers, see page

Smells Like . . .

Use some of the words from the word bank to describe what you think Martha smells like in this picture. Can you tell a story about how she got that way?

_____

_____

_____

_____

_____

_____

_____

_____

The Canine Crime Caper

T.D. and Martha had fun writing their story about the deserted hot dog. Now you can help Martha create a *comic strip*. A comic strip tells a story through a series of pictures illustrating the action, with speech or thought bubbles helping to tell the story. Fill in the speech and thought bubbles on these two pages to tell a story.

The day Martha passed the police station, she noticed two Wanted posters.

Later that same day, Martha and Helen peered into the closed jewelry store to see . . .

Martha took quick action.

awooooo...

All the dogs heard her call.

The crooks surrendered.

Martha Mail

Martha loves to get mail—don't you? You can use letters to tell people that you are thinking about them, to share some news, or to thank them for a present or for doing something nice. You can write a letter to Martha, a friend, or family member using the special stationery on the facing page (ask an adult to help you remove the page from the book).

A letter is made up of three main parts.
1. The greeting: *Dear So-and-So*
2. The body: the main part of the letter, where you tell the reader why you are writing to them
3. The closing: where you say goodbye (you can choose from different closings such as *Love*, *Sincerely*, *Best wishes*, or *Fondly*, followed by your signature)

It is a good idea to put the date at the top so they know when you sent the letter. Although Martha doesn't read, she can always count on a friend to read her the letters she receives.

If you do write a letter to Martha, she would love to receive it. Address it to

Susan Meddaugh
C/o HMH Books
222 Berkeley Street
Boston, MA 02116

_____
(date)

Dear_____ ,
(greeting)

_____

_____

_____

_____

_____

_____

_____

_____

_____

_____

_____

_____

_____ ,
(closing)

_____
(signature)

Added Attractions

When two words are joined together, they form a compound word. One of Martha's favorites is ham + burger = hamburger! Can you complete the compound words below? There may be more than one answer!

Ham   +   burger   =   hamburger

Fire   + _____ = _____
1

_____ + made = _____
2

Pepper   + _____ = _____
3

_____ + ground = _____
4

foot   + _____ = _____
5

_____ + case = _____
6

back   + _____ = _____
7

For answers, see page 32.

Author, Author!

Are you ready to write your own Martha adventure? We've provided some illustrations and some sentences to get you started. You provide the rest of the story.

Every story has a *beginning, middle,* and an *end.* In the beginning, you introduce your characters (who is in your story?) and you describe the setting (when and where does your story take place?). In the middle, the character or characters face a problem. How do they try to solve it? In the end, the problem is solved or all the questions are answered, and hopefully your main character lives happily ever after!

Before you start, look through all the pages and pictures. Think about what your story is going to be about and how the pictures help tell the story. Make your story more exciting by using interesting and unusual words. The word bank includes some examples to start your thinking. (You can check the glossary on pages 30-31 for definitions.) But don't stop there. Use your imagination and have fun!

_____

Title

by

_____

Author (that's you!)

Puppy Martha waited anxiously. Slowly she was being lowered through the skylight of the Wagstaff City Museum. Some crooks had taken Martha from the animal shelter and wanted to force her to steal a priceless dinosaur skeleton. It was late at night, and she couldn't see through the eerie darkness. Uh-oh, the rope was stuck!

_____

_____

_____

_____

_____

_____

_____

_____

_____

_____

Whew, she was finally on the floor.

Martha waited while her eyes got used to the dark. Suddenly she gasped. All she could see was_____

_____

_____

_____

_____

_____

_____

_____

_____

What should she do? Gathering her courage, she crept silently toward one of the dinosaur bones. Then_____

_____

_____

_____

_____

_____

_____

_____

_____

Just when Martha thought no one could help her, _____

_____

_____

_____

_____

_____

_____

_____

_____

_____

_____

THE END

Martha Masterpiece

You can create your own illustrated Martha storybooks. The first step is to practice drawing Martha. Look at the picture of Martha on this page and follow the grid. Copy the lines in each square into the same place on the facing page. This grid method works for copying or enlarging any picture.

Once you finish copying the picture of Martha, color her in!

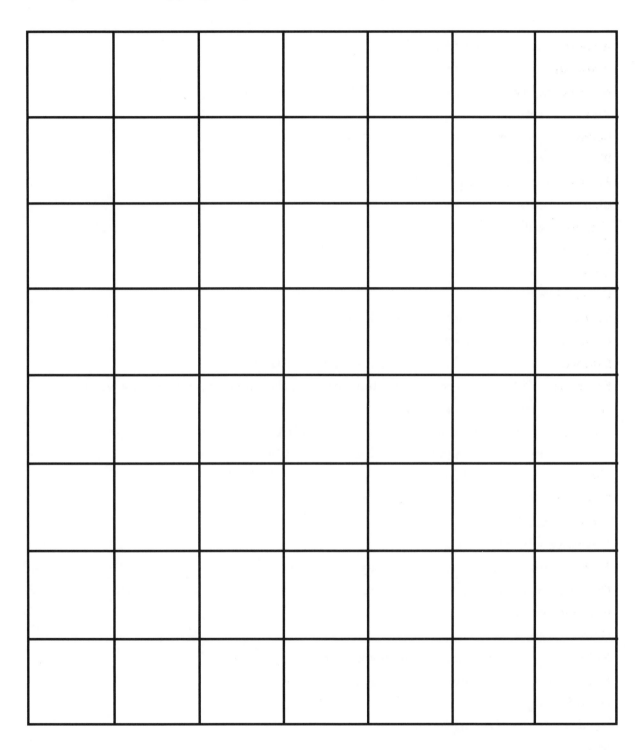

illustration   29

These definitions are particular to the context, and part of speech, in which the words are used within these workbooks. Many of these words have other meanings besides the ones provided.

GLOSSARY

Anxious Worried about something.

Astonish To strike with surprise and amazement.

Autobiography The true story of your life as written by you.

Awe Amazement.

Bacon A kind of meat that Martha loves to eat.

Bit A very small amount.

Bizarre Very odd; strange.

Blah Nonsense.

Canine Dog-like or relating to dogs.

Code A secret language.

Cozy Comfortable and warm.

Creepy Eerie; spooky.

Crouch To bend your knees and get close to the ground.

Exhausted Very, very tired.

Explore To travel around and find out what a place is like.

Expressions Phrases that mean something besides the literal meaning of the words.

Fair A carnival, festival, or celebration.

Fantasy Something you think about and want to happen, but which probably won't; something that is not based on what is real.

Fly A small bug with wings.

Foul Disgusting or gross.

Found Discovered.

Fragrance A pleasant smell.

Free Something you do not have to pay money for.

Fresh Clean and bright, not stale or moldy.

Garbage Trash.

Glum Sad and quiet.

Hold To carry or grasp something in your hands.

Honey Sweet, gooey liquid made by bees.

Hound A dog; canine.

Howl A long, loud crying sound.

Joke A funny story or trick.

Loon A fish-eating bird.

Mellow Calm; relaxed.

Mill To grind or crush.

Mint A plant whose leaves are used as a flavoring.

Money Paper or coins used to buy items.

Odor A scent or smell.

Ordinary Normal, what you expect; not special or different.

Path A trail, lane, or small road for walking.

Perfume An agreeable or sweet smell.

Poem An artistic piece of writing that often rhymes.

Queasy Sick to your stomach; nauseous.

Remember To think about something that happened a while ago.

Render To depict or make a copy.

Ride A short journey or trip.

Rose A beautiful flower with a pleasant scent.

Runny Gooey.

Scent A distinct smell, usually pleasant.

Setting Location, scenery, or background in a story, play, or movie.

Split To go; to do something quickly.

Spooky Scary; unnatural.

Soak To put something in liquid and leave it there.

Sniff To inhale, or to smell something.

Stage A raised platform that actors or musicians stand on to perform.

Stair A series of steps leading up or down.

Startle To surprise and frighten a little.

Stench An unpleasant, stinky smell.

Step A flat object to stand or walk on.

Strange Odd; unusual.

Stroke To pet.

Sweet Pleasing.

Thrilling Very exciting.

Under Beneath; below.

Unique One of a kind; very unusual or special.

ANSWER KEY

Page 2-Endless Expressions

1	E
2	A
3	G
4	K
5	J
6	B
7	C
8	I
9	L
10	H
11	D
12	F

1. Even though Helen had lots of homework, she wanted to be part of the school play. "**Don't bite off more than you can chew**, Helen," warned Mom.

2. Martha ran around in circles. "Come on, Helen. Hurry!" she said. "The free burger samples will be gone before we get there!" Helen shook her head. "Boy, Martha, you sure are **full of beans** today!"

3. "But it was such a good idea," Alice said. "I was sure it would work. I guess we should just **throw in the towel**." "No," Helen replied, "I still want to do it. But I guess we have to **go back to the drawing board**."

4. Martha and Helen were soaking wet, waiting under a tree at the playground. "There I was," Martha said, "**snug as a bug on a rug**, but you thought we should go for a walk!" "I'm sorry, Martha," Helen said. "I didn't know it was supposed to rain." Just then they heard a rumble of thunder in the distance. "Oh no, now we're really **in a pickle!**"

Page 12

Page 14-What's That Smell?

Page 21-Added Attractions
1. fireplace, firefly
2. homemade, handmade
3. peppermill, peppermint
4. underground, fairground
5. footpath, footstep
6. bookcase, staircase
7. backstage, backhand